Understanding English

Key Stage 2
Spelling

Carol Matchett

Name _____

Schofield & Sims

Introduction

Being able to spell is important because it makes your writing easier to read. If lots of words are spelt wrongly it is difficult for the reader to follow what you have written. Being able to spell also helps you as a writer. If you can spell words easily you can spend more time thinking about what you are writing.

This book will improve your spelling. It starts with things to look for when you are learning to spell and then gives you useful rules to follow.

Finding your way around this book

Before you start using this book, write your name in the name box on the first page.

Then decide how to begin. If you want a complete course on spelling, you should work right through the book from beginning to end. Another way to use the book is to dip into it when you want to find out about a particular topic. The contents page will help you to find the pages you need.

Whichever way you choose, don't try to do too much at once – it's better to work through the book in short bursts.

When you have found the topic you want to study, look out for these icons, which mark different parts of the text. **You may find it useful to have a dictionary near you so that you can check any spellings you are not sure about.**

Activities

This icon shows you the activities that you should complete. You write your answers in the spaces provided. After you have worked through all the activities on the page, turn to pages 33 to 40 to check your answers. When you are sure that you understand the topic, put a tick in the box beside it on the Contents page.

The **Revision** section on pages 30 and 31 will remind you of the topics covered by this book. On page 32 you will find suggestions for some projects (**Now you try!**), which will give you further practice in spelling.

Explanation

This text explains the topic and gives examples. Read it before you start the activities.

Information

This text gives you useful background information about the subject. Surprise your friends with some fascinating facts!

Contents

Tick the box
when you
have worked
through
the topic.

Looking at words

This book will show you how to improve your spelling by **learning to spell words** and by remembering **spelling rules**. Another way of improving your spelling is to **check** everything you write for mistakes.

We often spell words by how they **sound**, but what a word **looks like** is also important. When you write a word, **look at it**. Being able to tell if a word **looks right** is the start to becoming a good speller.

1. Look closely at the words in these sentences. One word in each sentence is spelt wrongly. Underline that word.

a) There were abowt seven of us in all.

b) We start back to sckuul next Tuesday.

c) There was wartter pouring all over the floor.

d) I wud have liked to go but I was too busy.

e) In the street peepel were shouting and cheering.

f) Simon saw the funny side and began to laff.

2. Draw round the outside shape of these words. Use the **shape** of each word to help you to picture it in your head.

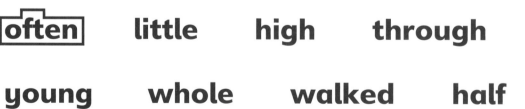

often   **little**   **high**   **through**

young   **whole**   **walked**   **half**

Did you know... The English alphabet is made up of 26 letters. Five of these are **vowels** (the letters 'a', 'e', 'i', 'o' and 'u'). The other letters are **consonants**. The 26 letters are used to make over 40 different sounds. Some make more than one sound and lots of the sounds are made by using different combinations of letters. This is why spelling can be difficult!

Learning to spell words

Many words, even little everyday words, are **not spelt as they sound**.

For example: w**a**s s**ai**d wh**a**t w**o**rk

But you will see that it is only **part** of these words that is difficult. With most words it is just a few letters that do not look like they sound. So you can learn to spell words by **looking** for the **tricky part** and learning to **picture it** in the word.

1. **Look closely** at each of these words. Underline the part of each word that you find tricky. Try to **picture** each word in your head.

friend	world	value	answer
surprise	colour	possible	sure
important	earth	people	because

2. Now that you have looked closely at the words in the box above, cover them up so you can't see them. Add the missing letters to these words.

a) val __ __   **c)** import __ __ t **e)** bec __ __ se   **g)** w __ __ __ d

b) fr __ __ nd   **d)** ans __ __ r   **f)** col __ __ r   **h)** p __ __ ple

3. Keep the words in the box covered. Tick the correct spelling of each of these words.

a) erth ☐   **b)** possible ☐   **c)** serprise ☐   **d)** shure ☐
earth ☐   posseble ☐   sarprise ☐   sure ☐
eerth ☐   possable ☐   surprise ☐   sewre ☐

When you have finished activities 2 and 3, check your answers against the correct spellings shown in activity 1.

Did you know... For hundreds of years, people spelt words how they wanted. It was only when more books were printed that people thought that fixed spellings might be a good idea. It was not until Samuel Johnson published his dictionary in 1755 that many spellings finally became fixed.

Common letter strings

Some words are hard to spell because they have difficult or unusual **strings of letters**. Sometimes you see the same string of letters in lots of words.

For example: c**ould** ▶ w**ould** ▶ sh**ould**

Once you have learned the letter string, you will be able to spell a whole group of words! Look out for words with the **same pattern** and **learn them together**.

1. Complete these word chains by adding other words with the **same letter string**.

a) (light) (__ight) (__ight) (__ight) (__ight)

b) | found | | | | |

c) (catch) ( ) ( ) ( ) ( )

d) | price | | | | |

2. Look at the words in the box below. Find the pairs of words that have the **same letter string**.

> air   brought   strange   flavour   change   rumour   fair   thought

Write the pairs of words below. For each pair, try to think of one extra word with the **same letter string**. Write the extra words in the second row of boxes.

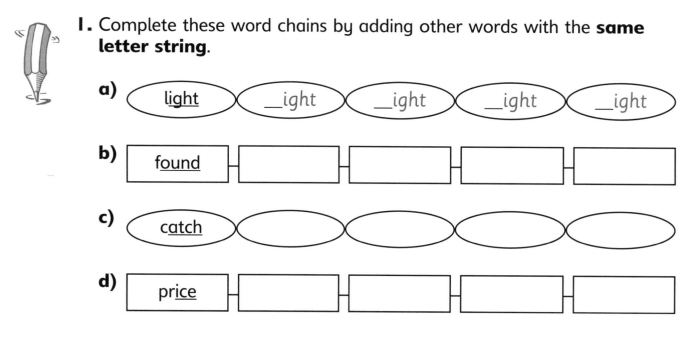

Syllables

Long words are made up of smaller parts called syllables. Syllables are like the beats in a word and **each syllable** has a **vowel** in it. Breaking words into syllables can help you to spell longer words. You can think separately about each part.

Some short words only have one syllable, while longer words may have lots.

For example:
     dog
     one syllable

     win / dow
     two syllables

     af / ter / noon
     three syllables

     in / vi / ta/ tion
     four syllables

     hip / po / pot / a / mus
     five syllables

1. Split these words into **syllables**. Draw a line between the syllables, like this:

a) garden ▶ *gar/den* _____

b) remember ▶ _____

c) following ▶ _____

d) information ▶ _____

e) problem ▶ _____

f) tomorrow ▶ _____

g) important ▶ _____

h) disgusting ▶ _____

i) operation ▶ _____

j) examination ▶ _____

2. Put the missing **syllable** into each of these words.

a) fan __ __ __ tic

b) en __ __ __ tain

c) un __ __ __ stand

d) for __ __ __ ten

e) sud __ __ __ ly

f) Sep __ __ __ ber

3. Put the missing **letters** into each of these words. Use the clues to help you.

a) u __ / b __ __ __ __ / l __   (Clue: Something we use when it rains.)

b) m __ __ / n __ __ __ __   (Clue: The first part of the day.)

c) i __ / t __ __ __ __ / i / g __ __ __   (Clue: Very clever.)

Words within words

Looking for **smaller words** inside long words will help you to remember how to spell them.

For example: intelligent ▶ in tell I gent
mother ▶ other moth her he the

1. See if you can find at least four **little words** inside these **longer words**. Write them in the box.

a) another ▶ [ ]

b) cardigan ▶ [ ]

c) shopping ▶ [ ]

d) dandelion ▶ [ ]

e) father ▶ [ ]

2. Complete these words by adding one of the **little words** from the box.

a) gar_____   **c)** sepa_____   **e)** toma _____

b) o_____ ge   **d)** con _____ ue   **f)** choco_____

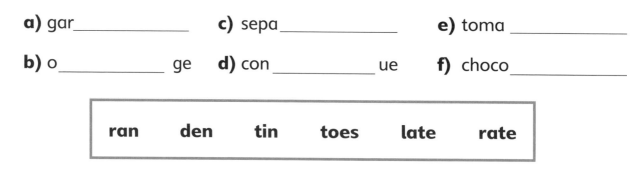

| ran | den | tin | toes | late | rate |

3. Underline a **three-letter word** in each of these longer words. Use this to help you remember how to spell the long word.

a) favourite   **c)** piece   **e)** money   **g)** friend

b) vegetable   **d)** listen   **f)** sandwich   **h)** believe

Compound words

Compound words are made up from **two words** that have been **put together** to make a new word.

For example: pop**corn**   play**ground**   tooth**brush**   snow**board**

The spelling of the two little words stays the same. So it is easier to spell compound words if you split them up into their two parts.

1. Complete these word sums to make **compound words**.

a) hand + bag =

b) shoe + lace =

c) space + craft =

d) cross + roads =

e) table + cloth =

f) post + card =

g) light + house =

h) earth + quake =

2. These compound words are all muddled up. Sort out the muddle by making eight real **compound words**. Write them in the box below.

windroom   **footfruit**   **headbrush**   **breakend**

weekfast   **bedmill**   **grapeball**   **hairquarters**

Did you know... Some compound words were formed so long ago that you might not recognise them as compound words at all. For example:

- *cloak* + *room* = *cloakroom* (from the time when people wore cloaks rather than coats)
- *hand* + *kerchief* = *handkerchief* (a *kerchief* was originally a square headscarf)
- *break* + *fast* = *breakfast* (*fast* meaning 'to go without food' – *breakfast* being the first meal of the day, when the fast is broken).

Unstressed vowels

Some words are tricky to spell because they have a **vowel** that you **cannot hear** when you say the word.

For example, say the word: carpet

It is difficult to hear the letter 'e' in the second part of this word. Even if you know that there must be a vowel between 'p' and 't', which vowel is it? Once you know that it is an 'e', you can remember to spell this word by saying 'car–pet'.

1. Say each of these words aloud in a normal voice. Underline the **vowel** that is likely to get missed out because it is **difficult to hear**.

a) animal

d) history

g) interest

b) family

e) freedom

h) important

c) library

f) factory

i) general

Say these words again. This time, make sure you can **hear the vowel** you have underlined.

2. Put in the **vowels** to complete these words. Use the clues to help you.

a) sk __ l __ t __ n   (Clue: Made up of bones.)

b) h __ l __ d __ y   (Clue: Time off from school or work.)

c) v __ g __ t __ bl __   (Clue: Farmers grow these for us to eat.)

d) s __ m __ l __ r   (Clue: Almost the same.)

e) fr __ ght __ n __ ng   (Clue: Very scary.)

3. Tick the correct spelling of each of these words.

a) company ☐   b) differant ☐   c) separate ☐   d) heavon ☐

company ☐   different ☐   seperate ☐   heavun ☐

compiny ☐   diffirent ☐   separate ☐   heaven ☐

Homophones

Homophones are words that **sound the same**, but are **not spelt the same** – and they have completely **different meanings**. The problem with spelling them is knowing which word is which.

For example:

steps going up and down ▶ stair　　and　　stare ◀ to look very hard

when something hurts ▶ sore　　and　　saw ◀ to have seen something

1. Read these two lists of words aloud. Join together the ones that sound the same. The first one is done for you.

poor	steal
sight	lone
loan	paw
steel	waist
aloud	site
waste	allowed

poor and _paw_

_____ and _____

_____ and _____

_____ and _____

_____ and _____

_____ and _____

2. Complete these pairs of **homophones**. The clues will help you.

a) write and _____ (Clue: The opposite of wrong.)

b) pear and _____ (Clue: Two of something.)

c) peace and _____ (Clue: A part of something.)

d) groan and _____ (Clue: When something has become larger.)

3. Put the correct **homophone** in each space so that these sentences make sense. Choose from the words in brackets at the end of each sentence.

a) The _____ bags were _____ heavy _____ carry. (to, too, two)

b) There were _____ letters _____ Jim. (for, four)

c) I can _____ a lot of noise coming from in _____ . (here, hear)

d) I _____ it was not my coat – mine was brand _____ . (new, knew)

Plurals

Plural means there is **more than one** of something. To change a word into a plural you usually **add –s** to the end of the word.

For example: one book ▶ lots of books   one car ▶ lots of cars

However, you sometimes have to **add –es**.

For example: bus ▶ buses   wish ▶ wishes   patch ▶ patches   tax ▶ taxes

If you listen to these words, you will hear a **hissing, buzzing** or **'ch' sound** at the end of the words. They would be difficult to say if you just added **–s**, so you need to add **–es** instead. This makes an 'is' sound at the end of the word.

1. Sort these words into the correct boxes. Then make each word into a **plural** by **adding –s or –es**.

~~apple~~ ~~torch~~ tree pencil box switch class chair spoon fox brush coat bear kiss straw fish	Ends with hissing, buzzing or 'ch' sounds		Ends with other sounds	
	• torches	•	• apples	•
	•	•	•	•
	•	•	•	•
	•	•	•	•

Some words that end with **–f** or **–fe** use **–ves** in the plural.

For example: one wol**f** ▶ lots of wol**ves**

2. Follow this rule to change these words to **plurals**.

a) One knife ▶ Six _____

b) One life ▶ Nine _____

c) One thief ▶ A gang of _____

d) One half ▶ Two _____

e) One leaf ▶ Hundreds of _____

f) One loaf ▶ Lots of _____

Plurals

Be careful with words that end with the letter –y.

If the letter **before the –y** is a **vowel** ('a', 'e', 'i', 'o' or 'u'), **just add –s. For example:** d<u>ay</u> ▶ days   k<u>ey</u> ▶ keys   b<u>oy</u> ▶ boys

But if the letter **before the –y** is a **consonant, drop the –y and add –ies. For example:** la<u>dy</u> ▶ ladies   pup<u>py</u> ▶ puppies

It would look very odd if you added **–ies** to a word that has a **vowel before the –y**.
For example: key ▶ keies ✗   keys ✓

3. Tick the correct spelling of each of these plurals.

a) toys ☐   toies ☐   **d)** spys ☐   spies ☐

b) chimneys ☐   chimneies ☐   **e)** dictionary ☐   dictionaries ☐

c) opportunitys ☐   opportunities ☐   **f)** holidays ☐   holidaies ☐

4. Use the spelling rules you have learned on pages 12 and 13 to help you rewrite this list as a list of plurals. The first one is done for you.

a) One plate   ▶ Eight <u>plates</u>

b) One dish   ▶ Eight_____

c) One glass   ▶ Eight_____

d) One lolly   ▶ 20_____

e) One box of chocolates   ▶ Two_____

f) One sandwich   ▶ 30_____

g) One strawberry   ▶ Lots of_____

h) One jelly   ▶ Two_____

i) One loaf of garlic bread   ▶ Two_____

Verbs ending with –ing

We often need to add **–ing** to the end of verbs. For most words this is easy. **For example:**

jump+ing = jumping   talk+ing = talking   try+ing = trying

But there are two special rules that you need to remember.

Rule 1: if the word **ends with the letter 'e', drop the 'e'** before adding **–ing. For example:**

make+ing = making   face+ing = facing   smile+ing = smiling

Rule 2: if the word **ends with a short vowel sound before a consonant, double the consonant** before adding **–ing. For example:**

hum+ing = humming   tap+ing = tapping   begin+ing = beginning

1. Use Rules 1 and 2 to help you sort these words into the three columns and add **–ing** to the end of each word. The first one is done for you.

hide	cook	beg	play	stop
shine	bake	shout	pin	like
throw	shop	swim	refuse	stamp

Just add –ing	Rule 1: drop the 'e'	Rule 2: double the consonant
	hide ▶ hiding	

Did you know...

The verb endings that we are familiar with today are –ing, –ed and –s (for example, *jumping, jumped, jumps*). Hundreds of years ago, there were other verb endings, such as –st, –est, –th and –eth. The verb ending –ed was sometimes written as –t, as in the word *kist,* or *blest.* You can see why this happened: it sounds like a –t when you say these words. Today, some verbs still sound as though they end with –t, but they are written with –ed. For example: *kissed, blessed, walked, talked.*

Verbs ending with –ed

We often add **–ed** to the end of a verb to show that something has already happened. **For example:**
jump+ed = jumped   talk+ed = talked   stay+ed = stayed.

You should already recognise the first two of the three rules to remember.
Rule 1: if the word **ends with 'e', drop the 'e'** before adding **–ed**.
For example: score+ed = scored   face+ed = faced   smile+ed = smiled

Rule 2: if the word ends with a **short vowel sound before a consonant, double the consonant** before adding **–ed**.
For example: h**um**+ed = hummed   t**ap**+ed = tapped   dr**op**+ed = dropped

1. Use Rules 1 and 2 to change the tense of these words by adding **–ed**.

a) like ▶ +ed ▶ _liked_   **d)** cook ▶ +ed ▶ _____

b) beg ▶ +ed ▶ _____   **e)** stop ▶ +ed ▶ _____

c) fade ▶ +ed ▶ _____   **f)** travel ▶ +ed ▶ _____

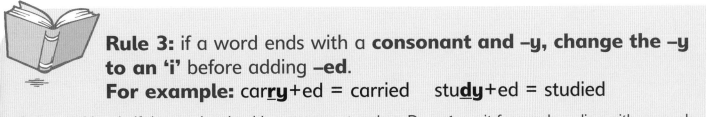

Rule 3: if a word ends with a **consonant and –y, change the –y to an 'i'** before adding **–ed**.
For example: car**ry**+ed = carried   stu**dy**+ed = studied

Only use this rule if the word ends with a consonant and –y. Do **not** use it for words ending with a vowel before the –y.

2. Tick the correct spelling of these words, using Rule 3 to help you.

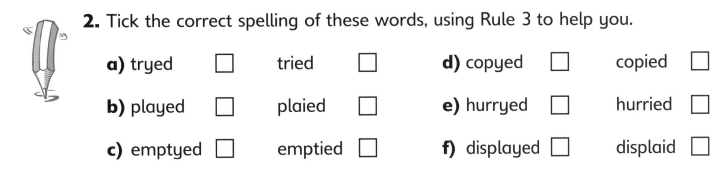

a) tryed ☐   tried ☐   **d)** copyed ☐   copied ☐

b) played ☐   plaied ☐   **e)** hurryed ☐   hurried ☐

c) emptyed ☐   emptied ☐   **f)** displayed ☐   displaid ☐

Prefixes

A prefix is a group of letters that can be **added to the beginning of a word**. A prefix changes the **meaning** of the word, but it does **not** change the **spelling**.

For example: un+kind = unkind   mis+behave = misbehave   re+visit = revisit

Spelling words like this is easy, as long as you know the prefix.

1. Complete these word sums. Just add the **prefix** to the beginning of the word.

a) mis+lead = _____

b) pre+view = _____

c) anti+freeze = _____

d) sub+way = _____

e) al+ready = _____

f) re+cycle = _____

g) dis+agree = _____

h) un+tidy = _____

i) de+frost = _____

j) al+together = _____

When the word *all* is used as a prefix, it is spelt al–, not all–

2. Choose the correct **prefix** to add to each of the words.

mis	anti	re	pre	non	ex	sub	al	dis

a) ☐ clockwise

b) ☐ historic

c) ☐ marine

d) ☐ most

e) ☐ sense

f) ☐ like

g) ☐ play

h) ☐ fortune

i) ☐ change

Did you know...
Over time, people have made many new words by adding prefixes to words that already existed. Many of the prefixes come from ancient languages, for example: *anti* (Greek, meaning 'against'); *mega* (Greek, meaning 'great' or 'large'); *sub* (Latin, meaning 'under'); *inter* (Latin, meaning 'between').

Prefixes

Here are two more things to remember about prefixes.
Some **prefixes** create words that have the **opposite** meaning.

For example:

perfect ▶**im**perfect   fair ▶**un**fair   complete ▶**in**complete

The spelling of the prefix and the word always stays the same, even if the prefix ends with the same letter as the word starts with.
For example: im+mature = **im**mature.

This explains why there is a **double letter**.

3. Complete the pairs of opposites by using these prefixes. You can use a prefix more than once.

dis	un	in	im	ir	il

a) visible and _____

b) appear and _____

c) well and _____

d) responsible and _____

e) patient and _____

f) possible and _____

g) legal and _____

h) obey and _____

i) likely and _____

j) dependent and _____

4. Think about the word and the prefix to help you decide if there should be a double letter in these words. Then tick the correct spelling.

a) iregular ☐
    irregular ☐

b) unatural ☐
    unnatural ☐

c) unecessary ☐
    unnecessary ☐

d) inhuman ☐
    innhuman ☐

e) disorder ☐
    dissorder ☐

f) imovable ☐
    immovable ☐

Suffixes

A **suffix** is a group of letters that can be added to the
end of a word.

For example:
care+**ful** = careful   music+**al** = musical   wash+**able** = washable

When the word full is used as a suffix it is spelt –ful rather than –full.

Sometimes two suffixes can be added to the end of a word.
For example: care+**ful**+**ly** = carefully   care+**ful**+**ness** = carefulness

1. Complete these word sums.

a) move+ment =

f) harm+less =

b) reason+able =

g) good+ness =

c) invent+ive =

h) hero+ic =

d) friend+ly =

i) play+ful =

e) pain+ful+ly =

j) person+al =

2. List all the words you can make from these **root words** and **suffixes**.

| Root words |
| enjoy   wind   hope |
| like   rest   king |
| hard   child |

| Suffixes |
| ment   less   ly |
| ness   hood   dom |
| able   ful   ship |

Words ending with –e

There are special rules for adding a suffix to **words ending with –e**.

If the **suffix begins with a vowel** ('a', 'e', 'i', 'o' or 'u'), **drop the –e** before adding the suffix. For this rule, the suffix **–y** also counts as a vowel suffix.

For example:

nature+**al** = natural   excuse+**able** = excusable   laze+**y** = lazy

If the **suffix begins with a consonant, keep the –e** and add the suffix.

For example:

love+**ly** = lovely   advertise+**ment** = advertisement

1. Use the rule to add these **suffixes** to the root words. The first one has been done for you.

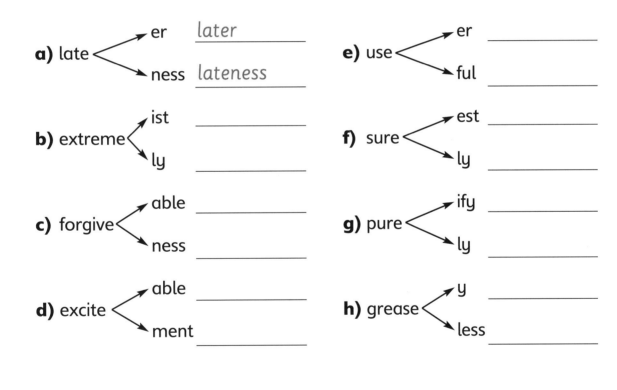

a) late — er — *later*
— ness — *lateness*

b) extreme — ist _____
— ly _____

c) forgive — able _____
— ness _____

d) excite — able _____
— ment _____

e) use — er _____
— ful _____

f) sure — est _____
— ly _____

g) pure — ify _____
— ly _____

h) grease — y _____
— less _____

Did you know...

There are always words that do not follow the rules. Here are a few examples of words that do not follow the spelling rules described above.

- Some words drop the –e when adding a consonant suffix:
  for example, argue+ment = *argument*.
- Some words keep the –e when adding a vowel suffix:
  for example, notice+able = *noticeable*.
- Some words can keep or drop the –e when adding a suffix:
  for example, move+able = *moveable* or *movable*.

Words ending with –y

There are also special rules for adding a suffix to a word ending with a **consonant followed by the letter –y**. In most cases, you **change the 'y' to an 'i'** when you add the suffix.

For example: happy+**ness** = happiness   happy+**er** = happier

If there is a **vowel before the final –y**, then you **just add the suffix**.

For example: pay+**ment** = payment   buy+**er** = buyer

1. Use the rule described above to add the suffix to these words. Write the correct spelling in the box.

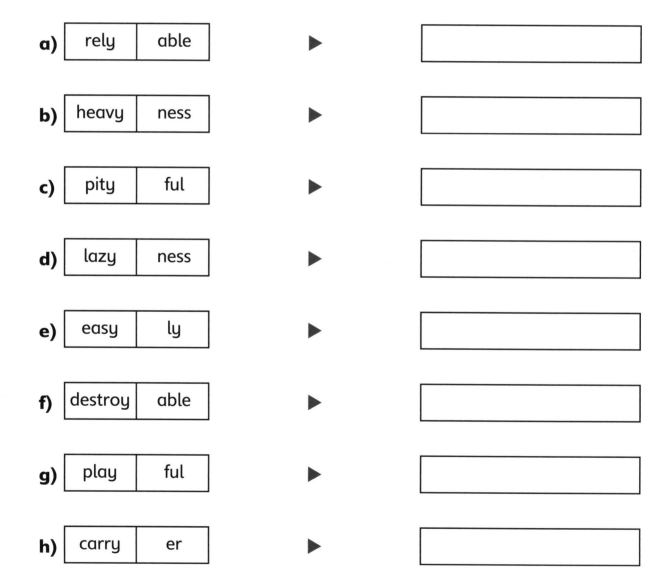

a) | rely | able | ▶

b) | heavy | ness | ▶

c) | pity | ful | ▶

d) | lazy | ness | ▶

e) | easy | ly | ▶

f) | destroy | able | ▶

g) | play | ful | ▶

h) | carry | er | ▶

Root words

Many longer words are made up of a short **root word** and a **prefix or suffix**. Looking for these is a good way of learning to spell longer words.

For example: unhelpfully can be broken down into the following parts:

un–	help	–ful	–ly
▲	▲	▲	
prefix	root word	suffixes	

It seems much easier to spell the word when you look at it like this!

1. Cross off any **prefixes** or **suffixes** and find the **root word** in these long words. The first one has been done for you.

a) ~~imperfection~~ ▶ `perfect`

b) disgracefully ▶

c) impolitely ▶

d) inexpensive ▶

e) dissatisfaction ▶

f) carefully ▶

g) refreshment ▶

h) disagreeable ▶

i) unattractive ▶

j) unfortunately ▶

2. Add **prefixes** and **suffixes** from the boxes to these **root words** – to make new words. Remember to use the rules about suffixes from pages 18, 19 and 20.

a) [ ] + kind + [ ] = [ ]

b) [ ] + turn + [ ] = [ ]

c) [ ] + rely + [ ] = [ ]

d) [ ] + expense + [ ] = [ ]

e) hope + [ ] + [ ] = [ ]

Prefixes	**Suffixes**
re– un– in–	–able –ly –ness
	–ive –ful –less

Words ending –tion, –sion or –ssion

Lots of words end with a 'shun' sound, but none of them are spelt –shun.

For example: direction discussion television

All the words end with the same sound, but the spelling is slightly different.

–tion is the ending you find **most often**. It is often **added to a verb** to make it into a noun.

For example: direct – direction

You will also find –tion added to shorter words, such as nation.

–ssion is formed when the root word ends with **'ss'**.

For example: discuss – discussion

–sion is usually found when the root word ends with **'s'**, **'se'**, **'d'** or **'de'**.

For example: televise – television   explode – explosion

1. Follow the rules above to sort these words into the right box and then write the word using the correct ending. The first one has been done for you.

correct	protect	revise	possess
divide	subtract	express	attract
confuse	inspect	invent	impress

–tion	–ssion	–sion
correction		

2. Write in the **vowel** that you can hear before the **–tion** in these words.

a) examin _ tion   **c)** repet _ tion   **e)** imagin _ tion   **g)** educ _ tion

b) convers _ tion   **d)** organis _ tion   **f)** pos _ tion   **h)** prom _ tion

Words ending –able or –ible

The –able and –ible endings cause a lot of confusion.

For example: move**able** laugh**able** poss**ible** vis**ible**

The endings of these words are spelt differently, but when you say them, the endings sound just the same!

A good clue is to think about the word without the ending.

If you take off the ending and are left with a **real word**, the spelling is most likely to be **–able**.

For example: moveable – **able** = move   laughable – **able** = laugh

There are a lot more words ending with –able than –ible.

If you take off the ending and what remains is **not a real word**, the spelling might well be **–ible**.

For example: possible – **ible** = poss   visible – **ible** = vis

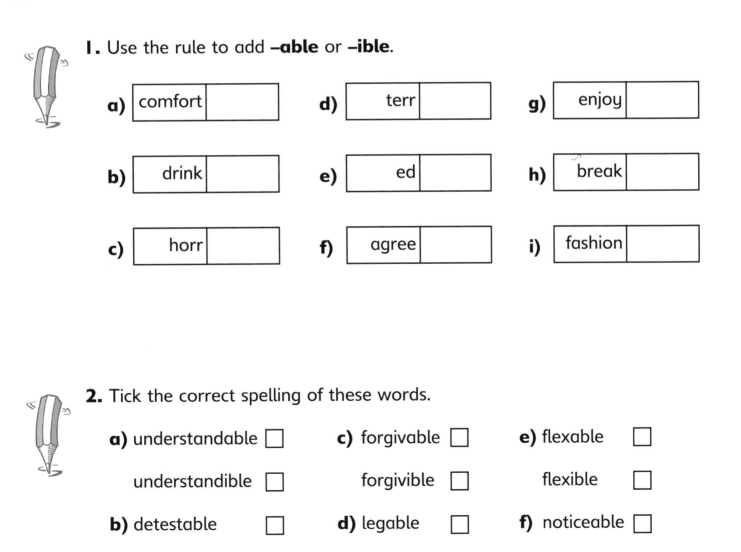

1. Use the rule to add **–able** or **–ible**.

a) comfort ____

b) drink ____

c) horr ____

d) terr ____

e) ed ____

f) agree ____

g) enjoy ____

h) break ____

i) fashion ____

2. Tick the correct spelling of these words.

a) understandable ☐
    understandible ☐

b) detestable ☐
    detestible ☐

c) forgivable ☐
    forgivible ☐

d) legable ☐
    legible ☐

e) flexable ☐
    flexible ☐

f) noticeable ☐
    noticeible ☐

Read aloud the four words below. Although they all seem to end with the same sound, the sound is made using different letters.

–le often follows **tall letters** or **descenders** (e.g. sensi**ble**, sin**gle**).

can**dle** ▶ More words use **–le** than the other endings.

id**ol** ▶ Only a few words end with **–ol**.

parc**el** ▶ **–el** often follows a **soft 'c'** or **soft 'g'**.

music**al** ▶ **–al** is often added to the end of a **root word**.

The pointers above will help you decide when to use each ending.

1. Use the pointers to help you decide which ending is needed for each of these words.

a) tick __ __   **d)** need __ __   **g)** magic __ __   **j)** horrib __ __

b) canc __ __   **e)** tab __ __   **h)** person __ __   **k)** simp __ __

c) tradition __ __   **f)** sett __ __   **i)** ang __ __   **l)** nation __ __

You can often decide between **–el** and **–le** by writing the word both ways and deciding which version **looks right**. For example, look at the shape of these words. Which one looks right?

Is it handel or handle? The correct spelling is han**dle**.

Notice that **–le** comes **after a tall letter**.

2. Draw round the shape of these words and tick the version that looks right.

a) terribel ☐   **b)** sparkel ☐   **c)** quarrel ☐

terrible ☐   sparkle ☐   quarrle ☐

Did you know... Rules like this are not straightforward. In most cases, the spelling of a word was fixed just because that was how most people spelt it. The rules were written *afterwards*! So there are always words that do not fit the rule.

Is it 'ie' or 'ei'?

The letters 'i' and 'e' are often found together. The problem is knowing whether the spelling is 'ie' or 'ei'. The rule **'i before e, except after c'** is very useful, but you need to know that it only works when the 'ie' or 'ei' makes a **long 'ee' sound**.

For example: th**ie**f   sh**ie**ld   dec**ei**ve

'i' before 'e'   'e' before 'i', because it comes after 'c'

If the letters make a **long 'ay' sound**, the spelling is usually 'ei'.

For example: n**ei**ghbour   v**ei**n

I. Use the rules above to help you tick the correct spelling of these words.

a) feild ☐   **d)** beleive ☐   **g)** ceiling ☐

field ☐   believe ☐   cieling ☐

b) cheif ☐   **e)** receive ☐   **h)** peice ☐

chief ☐   recieve ☐   piece ☐

c) weigh ☐   **f)** neice ☐   **i)** eight ☐

wiegh ☐   niece ☐   ieght ☐

2. Underline the misspelt word in this sentence.

The chief was relieved to escape
from the fierce battle. **X**

Did you know... Many vowel sounds can be spelt in more than one way – for example, the long 'ee' sound can be made by the letters 'ie' (*thief*), 'ee' (*feet*), 'ea' (*seat*) or 'e-e' (*here*). Also, the same spelling can make more than one sound – as we have seen with the letters 'ei'. The differences between spelling and pronunciation are partly because the way people say vowel sounds has changed in the last 450 years, but the spelling of some words was already fixed before these changes. Once the spelling of a word has been fixed, it is difficult to change.

Double consonants

Knowing whether a word has one or two consonants in the middle can be confusing, but there is a rule that will help you.

Read these words aloud and listen to the **vowel sound** that comes **before the double letters**.

dinner   supper   happy   rotten   better

All these double-letter words have a **short vowel** sound before the double letter.

The **short vowel** sound tells you that a **double letter** is needed.

If you hear a **long vowel sound**, there is only **one consonant**.

For example: diner   super

1. Write the correct spelling of the missing words in the sentence.

a) I fell asleep as soon as my head touched the _____ . (pilow, pillow)

b) I know a really _____ joke. (funy, funny)

c) The _____ is only six weeks old. (baby, babby)

d) We went for a _____ in the sea. (padle, paddle)

e) The horse was kept in a _____ . (stable, stabble)

f) I _____ I could meet you later. (supose, suppose)

g) Would you like a mug of _____ ? (cofee, coffee)

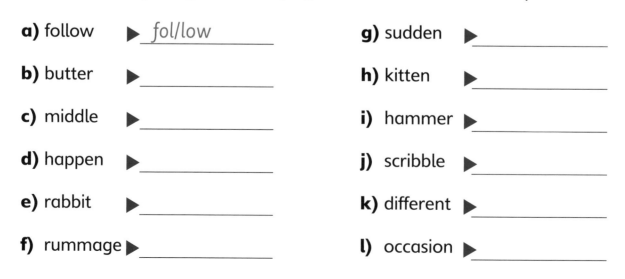

2. Break these words into **syllables**. The break comes **between the two consonants**. Splitting words helps you to remember how to spell them.

a) follow   ▶ _fol/low_

b) butter   ▶ _____

c) middle   ▶ _____

d) happen   ▶ _____

e) rabbit   ▶ _____

f) rummage ▶ _____

g) sudden   ▶ _____

h) kitten   ▶ _____

i) hammer   ▶ _____

j) scribble   ▶ _____

k) different ▶ _____

l) occasion   ▶ _____

Soft and hard letter sounds

Some letters have more than one sound, and this can cause problems in spelling.

The letter 'c' makes a **hard sound** if it is followed by **'a'**, **'o'** or **'u'**.

For example: cat   can   copy   cot   cup   cuddle

The letter 'c' makes a **soft sound** (like the letter 's') if it is followed by the letters **'e'**, **'i'** or **'y'**.

For example: ceiling   city   cyberspace

Exactly the **same rule** applies to the **letter 'g'**.

1. Read these words aloud. Draw a circle around each word that has a **soft 'c'**, which sounds like the letter 's' in *soap*. Then underline the **letter that follows the soft 'c'** to check the rule.

circle	card	cave	cell	pencil	cup
cylinder	candle	palace	bacon	Cyprus	

2. Now read these words aloud. Draw a circle around each word that has a **soft 'g'**, which sounds like the letter 'j' in *jelly*. Then underline the **letter that follows the soft 'g'** to check the rule.

gold	gentle	gate	gym	gutter
giraffe	game	ginger	general	

3. Put the missing letters into these words.

    a) re ＿ ＿ pe   (Clue: Found in a cookbook.)

    b) ex ＿ ＿ llent   (Clue: Very, very good.)

    c) ur ＿ ＿ nt   (Clue: Needed immediately.)

    d) ima ＿ ＿ ne   (Clue: To picture in your mind.)

Did you know... The 's' sound is still more likely to be made by the letter 's' than by a soft 'c'. So don't get too carried away!

Silent letters

Some words have 'silent' letters, which you cannot hear when you say the word.

Read these words aloud: **k**now **g**nome **w**rite thum**b** ha**l**f w**h**at

You cannot hear the silent letter, so you have to know how to spell these words or recognise what they look like.

Look out for patterns that go with silent letters, **for example**:

* **silent 'k'** and **silent 'g'** are often **followed by the letter 'n'**
* **silent 'w'** is often **followed by the letter 'r'**
* **silent 'b'** comes **after the letter 'm'**.

1. Read these words aloud. Draw a line under the silent letter.

    a) lamb   **c)** yolk   **e)** wrong   **g)** gnaw   **i)** knee

    b) knot   **d)** fasten   **f)** guest   **h)** wreck   **j)** debt

2. Which silent letter is missing from each of these sentences?

    a) The _night had a _nack with _nitting. | silent letter: |

    b) Lis_en to the whis_le of the wind through the cas_le. | silent letter: |

    c) I _rote the _rong address on the _rapper. | silent letter: |

3. Put in the silent letter that is missing from each of these words.

    a) ☐ nock   **d)** s ☐ ord   **g)** crum ☐

    b) ca ☐ m   **e)** ☐ rinkle   **h)** ☐ narled

    c) ☐ nife   **f)** bom ☐   **i)** ans ☐ er

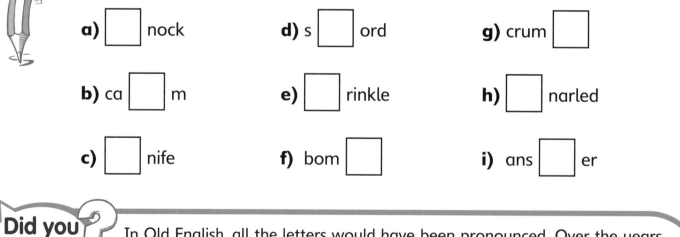

Did you know... In Old English, all the letters would have been pronounced. Over the years, we have changed how we say the words, but sometimes the original spelling has been kept. Here are some examples of what Old English would have looked like: *Giese* ('Yes'), *wilcume* ('Welcome!'), *Ie grete þe* ('I greet you! / Hello!')

Letter rules

There are very clear rules about certain letters: try and remember them.

Rule 1: the **letter 'q'** is always followed by a **'u'** and **another vowel**.

Rule 2: the **letter 'v'** is always followed by a **vowel** and is **never found at the end** of a word.

A 'v' sound at the end of a word is usually spelt –ve.

Rule 3: English words **do not usually end with a 'j'**.

If you hear a 'j' sound at the end of a word, it is usually spelt –ge or –dge.

Rule 4: words in the English language **do not usually end with 'i' or 'u'**.

1. Use the rules to help you circle the correct spelling of these words.

a) qwilt   qilt   qult   quilt   qwuilt

b) qalify   qualifi   qualify   qwalify   cwalify

c) qwiver   quiver   quver   quivr   qiuver

Did you know... Hundreds of years ago, the sound made by the letters 'qu' was written 'cw': for example, *cwic* ('*quick*'). The Norman invasion in 1066 brought the French language to Britain and from that time onwards the French spelling of 'qu' was used.

2. Use the rules to help you solve these anagrams.

a) seva _____ (Clue: If you keep something, you____ it.)

b) lenov _____ (Clue: A story – usually long and written in chapters.)

c) epi _____ (Clue: It could be an apple one or a chicken one.)

d) qeuka _____ (Clue: To tremble.)

e) vlaeu _____ (Clue: What something is worth.)

Did you know... Although English words do not usually end with 'i' or 'u', some words break this rule because they come from other languages: for example, *kiwi, ski, khaki, zulu*. Some other words taken from different languages also have unusual spelling patterns: for example, *banana, piano, giraffe, anorak*.

Revision

These pages will help you to check how well you can remember the spelling rules. If you can't remember the rules, the page numbers are given so that you can go back and reread them.

1. Plurals (pages 12–13)
Write the plural of each of these words.

a) hiss _____

b) lunch _____

c) watch _____

d) life _____

e) scarf _____

f) wife _____

g) cry _____

h) party _____

i) nappy _____

j) box _____

The words below have been written down as they sound, but all the spellings are wrong. You need to write the correct spelling of each word.

2. Verb endings (pages 14–15)

a) driveing _____

b) amazeing _____

c) hopet _____

d) sliping _____

e) runing _____

f) claped _____

g) criing _____

h) staid _____

i) scurryid _____

j) driping _____

Revision

3. Root words, prefixes and suffixes (pages 16–21)

a) dissappear _____

b) alltogether _____

c) actsion _____

d) forgetfull _____

e) nicly _____

f) pavment _____

g) heavyly _____

h) emptyness _____

i) discusstion _____

j) noticable _____

4. Making choices (pages 22–25)

a) creasion _____

b) pollussion _____

c) collition _____

d) spreadible _____

e) horrable _____

f) greif _____

g) exampel _____

h) troubel _____

i) tunnle _____

j) petral _____

5. Tricky letters (pages 26–29)

a) bom _____

b) strugle _____

c) hapen _____

d) sertificate _____

e) nowledg _____

f) qwiz _____

g) jem _____

h) forgiv _____

i) bridj _____

j) thum _____

Now you try!

Here are some games and activities that will help you to look at words more closely and improve your spelling.

Hangman

Playing a game of hangman is a good way to **learn spellings**. Choose words linked to a topic that you are working on at school. Change the rules slightly so that you have to guess the letters in the correct order. This will help you to build up a **picture of the word**.

Word hunt

Here is a word game that you can play when you are out shopping. Choose the name of a shop (for example, Morrisons). Look at the name carefully and see how many **little words** you can find inside it (Morris, son, on, or, is).

Post-it spelling

If you are given a list of spellings to learn, try this. Write each of the words on a post-it. **Look** at each word carefully and underline the **tricky part** of the word. Get a good **picture** of the word in your head. Then stick the post-it under the table so that you can't see it. Try writing the word, and then check whether you were right. You can also stick the post-its round your room to keep reminding you of what the words look like.

Beat the spell-check

If you have a computer at home, use the word processor to type a few sentences. **Look** carefully at what you have written and see if you can find any **mistakes** in your spelling. Then use the spell-check to see if the words you picked out are spelt wrongly.

Two letters and a vowel

If you have a little brother or sister, ask if you can borrow his or her plastic or sponge letters. Separate out the vowels and then pick out **one vowel** and **two other letters** (e.g. 'c', 'i', 'm'). The task is then to think of a word that includes those letters (for example, *ci*ne*m*a, *c*li*m*b).

Grand Scrabble Championships

To be a Grand Scrabble Champion you need to know lots of words and be able to spell them. While you are practising, it is OK to use a **dictionary** to help you.

Answers

1.
a) There were **abowt** seven of us in all.
b) We start back to **sckuul** next Tuesday.
c) There was **wartter** pouring all over the floor.
d) I **wud** have liked to go but I was too busy.
e) In the street **peepel** were shouting and cheering.
f) Simon saw the funny side and began to **laff**.

You can check your answers to the questions on page 5 by looking at the correct spellings in the box beneath activity 1.

1. *Here are some words that you may have included in your word chains. Remember that the order of the words does not matter, and that there may be other words you could have used. If you have chosen different words, check in your dictionary to see if you have spelt them correctly.*

a) l**ight** – f**ight**, s**ight**, r**ight**, br**ight**, etc.
b) f**ound** – s**ound**, r**ound**, gr**ound**, h**ound**, etc.
c) c**atch** – m**atch**, h**atch**, p**atch**, sn**atch**, etc.
d) pr**ice** – n**ice**, m**ice**, d**ice**, r**ice**, etc

2. *Here are the pairs of words with the same letter string.*
Underneath each pair you will see two more words with the same letter string – but you only need one extra word to get the activity right.
If you have chosen different words, check in a dictionary to see if you have spelt them correctly.

- **air**
- f**air**

- br**ought**
- th**ought**

- str**ange**
- ch**ange**

- flav**our**
- rum**our**

- ch**air**
- h**air**

- b**ought**
- f**ought**

- r**ange**
- gr**ange**

- col**our**
- lab**our**

1.
a) gar/den
b) re/mem/ber
c) fol/low/ing
d) in/for/ma/tion
e) prob/lem
f) to/mor/row
g) im/por/tant
h) dis/gus/ting
i) o/per/a/tion
j) ex/am/in/a/tion

2.
a) fan/**tas**/tic
b) en/**ter**/tain
c) un/**der**/stand
d) for/**got**/ten
e) sud/**den**/ly
f) Sep/**tem**/ber

3.
a) um/br**el**/la
b) m**or**/n**ing**
c) in/**tell**/i/g**ent**

Answers

Page 8

1.
a) another ▶ an other no not the her he a
b) cardigan ▶ car dig an card a I
c) shopping ▶ shop hop hopping pin in
d) dandelion ▶ an and lion on a I
e) father ▶ fat the he her a at

2.
a) gar**den**
b) or**an**ge
c) sepa**rate**
d) con**tin**ue
e) toma**toes**
f) choco**late**

3.
a) fav**our**ite
b) ve**get**able
c) **pie**ce
d) lis**ten**
e) m**one**y
f) s**and**wich
g) fri**end**
h) be**lie**ve

Page 9

1.
a) handbag
b) shoelace
c) spacecraft
d) crossroads
e) tablecloth
f) postcard
g) lighthouse
h) earthquake

2. *These are the eight compound words, though you may have written them in a different order.*

windmill	football	headquarters	breakfast
weekend	bedroom	grapefruit	hairbrush

Page 10

1.
a) anim**a**l
b) fam**i**ly
c) libr**a**ry
d) hist**o**ry
e) freed**o**m
f) fact**o**ry
g) int**e**rest
h) import**a**nt
i) gen**e**ral

2.
a) sk**ele**ton
b) h**o**liday
c) ve**ge**table
d) simil**a**r
e) fright**e**ning

3. *You should have ticked the following spellings.*
a) comp**a**ny
b) diff**e**rent
c) sep**a**rate
d) heav**e**n

Page 11

1.
poor — paw
sight — site
loan — lone
steel — steal
aloud — allowed
waste — waist

poor and paw
sight and site
loan and lone
steel and steal
aloud and allowed
waste and waist

2.
a) right
b) pair
c) piece
d) grown

34 Spelling

Schofield & Sims | Understanding English

Answers

3. a) The **two** bags were **too** heavy **to** carry.
   b) There were **four** letters **for** Jim.
   c) I can **hear** a lot of noise coming from in **here**.
   d) I **knew** it was not my coat – mine was brand **new**.

Page 12 1.

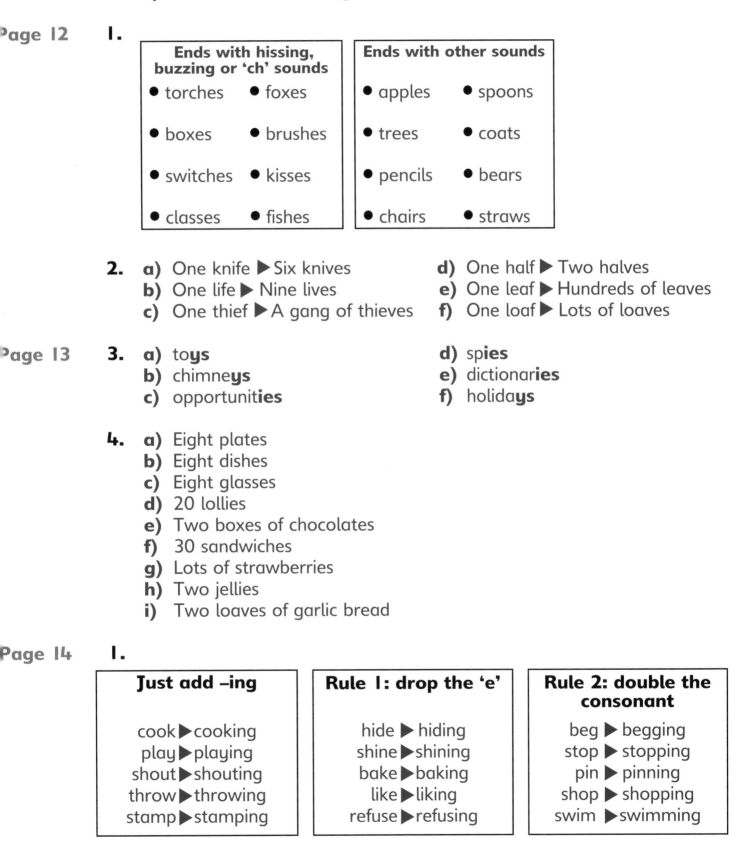

Ends with hissing, buzzing or 'ch' sounds		Ends with other sounds	
● torches	● foxes	● apples	● spoons
● boxes	● brushes	● trees	● coats
● switches	● kisses	● pencils	● bears
● classes	● fishes	● chairs	● straws

2. a) One knife ▶ Six knives
   b) One life ▶ Nine lives
   c) One thief ▶ A gang of thieves
   d) One half ▶ Two halves
   e) One leaf ▶ Hundreds of leaves
   f) One loaf ▶ Lots of loaves

Page 13 3. a) to**ys**
   b) chimne**ys**
   c) opportunit**ies**
   d) sp**ies**
   e) dictionar**ies**
   f) holida**ys**

4. a) Eight plates
   b) Eight dishes
   c) Eight glasses
   d) 20 lollies
   e) Two boxes of chocolates
   f) 30 sandwiches
   g) Lots of strawberries
   h) Two jellies
   i) Two loaves of garlic bread

Page 14 1.

Just add –ing	Rule 1: drop the 'e'	Rule 2: double the consonant
cook ▶ cooking	hide ▶ hiding	beg ▶ begging
play ▶ playing	shine ▶ shining	stop ▶ stopping
shout ▶ shouting	bake ▶ baking	pin ▶ pinning
throw ▶ throwing	like ▶ liking	shop ▶ shopping
stamp ▶ stamping	refuse ▶ refusing	swim ▶ swimming

Answers

Page 15

1.
a) liked
b) begged
c) faded
d) cooked
e) stopped
f) travelled

2.
a) tr**ied**
b) pla**yed**
c) empt**ied**
d) cop**ied**
e) hurr**ied**
f) displa**yed**

Page 16

1.
a) mislead
b) preview
c) antifreeze
d) subway
e) already
f) recycle
g) disagree
h) untidy
i) defrost
j) altogether

2.
a) anticlockwise
b) prehistoric
c) submarine
d) almost
e) nonsense
f) dislike
g) replay *or* display
h) misfortune
i) exchange

Page 17

3.
a) invisible
b) disappear
c) unwell
d) irresponsible
e) impatient
f) impossible
g) illegal
h) disobey
i) unlikely
j) independent

4.
a) ir**r**egular
b) un**n**atural
c) un**n**ecessary
d) i**n**human
e) di**s**order
f) i**mm**ovable

Page 18

1.
a) movement
b) reasonable
c) inventive
d) friendly
e) painfully
f) harmless
g) goodness
h) heroic
i) playful
j) personal

2. *Here are some of the words you may have made – the order of the words in your list does not matter. If you have made any other words, check them in a dictionary.*

enjoyable	likeness	kingship
enjoyment	likeable	hardly
windless	restless	hardness
hopeless	restful	hardship
hopeful	kingly	childless
likely	kingdom	childhood

Answers

Page 19 **1.** **a)** later
lateness

e) user
useful

b) extremist
extremely

f) surest
surely

c) forgivable
forgiveness

g) purify
purely

d) excitable
excitement

h) greasy
greaseless

Page 20 **1.** **a)** reliable   **e)** easily
b) heaviness   **f)** destroyable
c) pitiful   **g)** playful
d) laziness   **h)** carrier

Page 21 **1.** **a)** perfect   **f)** care
b) grace   **g)** fresh
c) polite   **h)** agree
d) expense *(don't forget the 'e' on the end!)*   **i)** attract
e) satisfy   **j)** fortune *or* fortunate

2. **a)** unkindly / unkindness
b) returnable
c) unreliable
d) inexpensive
e) hopelessly / hopelessness / hopefully / hopefulness

Page 22 **1.**

–tion	–ssion	–sion
correction	possession	revision
protection	expression	division
subtraction	impression	confusion
attraction		
inspection		
invention		

2. **a)** examin**a**tion **c)** repet**i**tion **e)** imagin**a**tion **g)** educ**a**tion
b) convers**a**tion **d)** organis**a**tion **f)** pos**i**tion **h)** prom**o**tion

Page 23 **1.** **a)** comfort**able** **d)** terr**ible** **g)** enjoy**able**
b) drink**able** **e)** ed**ible** **h)** break**able**
c) horr**ible** **f)** agree**able** **i)** fashion**able**

Answers

2.   **a)** understand**able**   **c)** forgiv**able**   **e)** flex**ible**
       b) detest**able**   **d)** leg**ible**   **f)** notice**able**

Page 24   **1.**   **a)** tick**le**   **d)** need**le**   **g)** magic**al**   **j)** horrib**le**
                      b) canc**el**   **e)** tab**le**   **h)** person**al**   **k)** simp**le**
                      c) tradition**al**   **f)** sett**le**   **i)** ang**le**/ang**el**   **l)** nation**al**

          2.   **a)** terrib**le**   **b)** spark**le**   **c)** quarr**el**

Page 25   **1.**   **a)** f**ie**ld   **d)** bel**ie**ve   **g)** c**ei**ling
                      b) ch**ie**f   **e)** rec**ei**ve   **h)** p**ie**ce
                      c) w**ei**gh   **f)** n**ie**ce   **i)** **ei**ght

          2.   The chief was <u>**releived**</u> to escape from the fierce battle.
                *(The correct spelling is **relieved**.)*

Page 26   **1.**   **a)** pillow
                      b) funny
                      c) baby
                      d) paddle
                      e) stable
                      f) suppose
                      g) coffee

          2.   **a)** fol/low   **g)** sud/den
                      b) but/ter   **h)** kit/ten
                      c) mid/dle   **i)** ham/mer
                      d) hap/pen   **j)** scrib/ble
                      e) rab/bit   **k)** dif/fer/ent
                      f) rum/mage   **l)** oc/ca/sion

Page 27   **1.**   *You should have drawn a circle around each of these words.*
                circle   **c**ell   pen**c**il
                cylinder   pala**c**e   **Cy**prus

          2.   *You should have drawn a circle around each of these words.*
                gentle   **gy**m
                giraffe   **gi**nger   **ge**neral

          3.   **a)** re**ci**pe
                      b) ex**ce**llent
                      c) ur**ge**nt
                      d) ima**gi**ne

Answers

Page 28

1. a) lam**b**   c) yo**l**k   e) **w**rong   g) **g**naw   i) **k**nee
b) **k**not   d) fas**t**en   f) g**u**est   h) **w**reck   j) de**b**t

2. a) **k**night   **k**nack   **k**nitting   – silent letter: **k**
b) lis**t**en   whis**t**le   cas**t**le   – silent letter: **t**
c) **w**rote   **w**rong   **w**rapper   – silent letter: **w**

3. a) **k**nock   d) s**w**ord   g) crum**b**
b) ca**l**m   e) **w**rinkle   h) **g**narled
c) **k**nife   f) bom**b**   i) ans**w**er

Page 29

1. a) quilt
b) qualify
c) quiver

2. a) save
b) novel
c) pie
d) quake
e) value

Page 30

1. Plurals
a) hisses   f) wives
b) lunches   g) cries
c) watches   h) parties
d) lives   i) nappies
e) scarves   j) boxes

2. Verb endings
a) driving   f) clapped
b) amazing   g) crying
c) hoped   h) stayed
d) slipping   i) scurried
e) running   j) dripping

Answers

3. Root words, prefixes and suffixes

a) disappear

b) altogether

c) action

d) forgetful

e) nicely

f) pavement

g) heavily

h) emptiness

i) discussion

j) noticeable

4. Making choices

a) creation

b) pollution

c) collision

d) spreadable

e) horrible

f) grief

g) example

h) trouble

i) tunnel

j) petrol

5. Tricky letters

a) bomb

b) struggle

c) happen

d) certificate

e) knowledge

f) quiz

g) gem

h) forgive

i) bridge

j) thumb